Pirates Coloring Book

Designed and illustrated by Candice "Quickdraw" Whatmore

Written by Kirsteen "Razor-quill" Rogers

Pirates Consultant: Tony "Blizzard Whiskers" Pawlyn

Coloring hints and tips

Use felt-tip pens or colored pencils to color in the pictures. Felt-tip pens will give you strong colors, while pencils will have a softer effect.

You can draw patterns within some of the shapes. For example, this scene is decorated with spots and dots...

...waves and wiggles...

...stripes.

You could finish this picture to practice coloring.

Fill in larger areas such as this island with lots of lines going in the same direction.

It's a good idea to lay your book on a flat surface while you are coloring, or slip a piece of cardboard under the page you are filling in, to make a firm surface.

LONG JOHN SILVER

Long John Silver was a fictional pirate from the book 'Treasure Island' by Robert Louis Stevenson. Silver's left leg had been cut off at the hip after a sea battle, but he hopped around very nimbly using a crutch. He had a parrot companion named Captain Flint who sat on his shoulder. In the book Silver and his shipmates trick their way onto an expedition in search of buried treasure.

Henry Morgan

Henry Morgan was a privateer which meant he had permission from the government to raid foreign ships. He became one of the richest pirates ever.

Black Bart

Nicknamed Black Bart, Bartholomew Roberts was a daredevil pirate famous for attacking ships that had more cannons than his. Unusually for a pirate, he was well known for preferring a tankard of tea to a tot of rum. He gained the reputation for being invincible – until his death four years into his pirate career.

BLACKBEARD

Blackbeard's real (but less terrifying) name was Edward Teach. To boost his already alarming image, he sometimes tucked burning ropes under his hat, cloaking himself in clouds of smoke.

Captain Hook

Captain James Hook is a character in J.M. Barrie's book 'Peter Pan.' The pirate's name refers to the large metal hook he wore in place of his right hand, which Peter Pan had cut off and fed to a crocodile. The croc liked the taste so much it followed Hook around, hoping to finish its meal.

MARY READ AND ANN BONNY

Women were strictly forbidden on pirate ships, so female pirates were rare. Mary Read and Ann Bonny disguised themselves as men and joined the pirate crew of a captain named Calico Jack. They fought even more fiercely than their male shipmates.